THE ENEMY INSIDE

Paul Blum

RISING STARS

Rising Stars UK Ltd.
22 Grafton Street, London W1S 4EX
www.risingstars-uk.com

nasen
Helping Everyone Achieve
■ ■■ ■   nasen

NASEN House, 4/5 Amber Business Village, Amber Close,
Amington, Tamworth, Staffordshire B77 4RP

Published 2008

Cover design: pentacorbig
Illustrator: Chris King, Illustration Ltd.
Text design and typesetting: pentacorbig
Publisher: Gill Budgell
Editor: Catherine Baker
Editorial project management: Margot O'Keeffe
Editorial consultant: Lorraine Petersen
Photos: Alamy

British Library Cataloguing in Publication Data.
A CIP record for this book is available from the British Library.

ISBN: 978-1-84680-455-7

Printed by Craft Print International Limited, Singapore

shadows

Contents

The Crash

- The Crash happened in 2021. Alien space ships crash landed on Earth.

- After The Crash, the Earth became very cold and dark.

- Now the aliens rule the world.

- The aliens have changed shape so they look like people.

- People call the aliens The Enemy.

Life after the Crash

- People are afraid.

- They do not know who is an Enemy and who is a friend.

The Firm

- The Firm keeps order on the streets.

- The Firm keeps people safe from Enemy attacks.

About Matt Merton

Matt Merton works
for The Firm. He
often works with
Dexter. Their job
is to find and kill
Enemy. They use
Truth Sticks to do this.

But Matt has problems.

Matt has lost his
memory. He cannot
answer some big
questions.

- Where has Jane, his
  girlfriend, gone?

- How did he get his job
  with The Firm?

Matt thinks The Firm is
on the side of good.
But is it?

chapter 1

Matt's phone rang. It was the Head of The Firm.

'Come to my office,' he said.

Matt took the sky tram to The Firm.

He looked down on the city.

It was always winter and never summer.

Matt felt nervous.

chapter 2

'I only have the best people working for me,'
said the Head of The Firm.

'Are you still one of the best, Matt?'

Matt did not know what to say.

The door opened. 'Here's Dexter. I want you to work with him this week,' said the Head.

'I know he is one of the best.

Dexter always finds The Enemy and he always kills them.'

Matt didn't like Dexter. Dexter didn't like Matt.

It was going to be a long week.

The Head of The Firm gave his orders.

'There is a spy in The Firm. The Enemy have got in. You two must find the spy.

You must question everyone.'

'Everyone?' asked Dexter.

'Everyone,' said the Head.

Dexter and Matt worked hard.

Day and night.

Night and day.

They followed the staff.

They followed the bosses.

They read their emails.

They heard their phone calls.

It was no good.

No spies.

No Enemy.

No leads.

Nothing.

Time was up. They hadn't found the spy.

Dexter was angry.

'Someone in here must know something,' he said.

'Wait, Dexter,' said Matt. 'Did you talk to the cleaner?'

Dexter said nothing.

'Did you hear me? Did you talk to the cleaner?'
Matt asked.

Now Matt was angry. The cleaner had 'the look'.
But Dexter had not spotted it.

They had to get him. They had to get him before he killed.

'Your name?' said Dexter.

The cleaner said nothing.

'Your birthday?' said Dexter.

The cleaner just looked away.

'Your mother's name?' said Dexter.

The cleaner smiled.

'You should be careful,' said the cleaner.
'Getting into The Firm was so easy.'

Dexter pointed the Truth Stick.
The job was done.

chapter 4

'I'm still the best man here, Matt. I always find The Enemy and kill them,' said Dexter.

'Yeah, right,' Matt said.

Matt went back to the bar. They had done good work, but Matt wanted answers.

Dexter just wanted to kill.

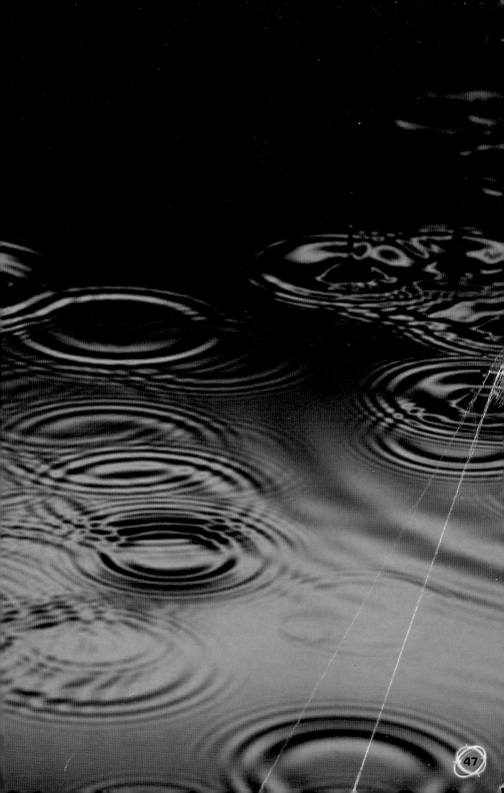

about the author

Hi Lo

AUTHOR NAME
Paul Blum

JOB
Teacher

LAST KNOWN LOCATION
North London, England

NOTES
Before The Crash taught in Inner-city London
schools. Writer of series of books called
The Extraordinary Files. Believed to be in
hiding from The Firm. Wanted for questioning.
Seems to know more about The Enemy than
he should ...